Riley's Yoga Walk

Story By
Cary Saltsgaver

Art By
Stacey Harris

Published by Hasmark Publishing International
www.hasmarkpublishing.com

Copyright 2020 Cary Saltsgaver and Stacey Harris
First Edition

Editor: Allison Burney
allison@hasmarkpublishing.com

Illustrations: Stacey Harris
staceyharrisart@gmail.com

Layout: Anne Karklins
anne@hasmarkpublishing.com

ISBN 13: 978-1-989756-71-3
ISBN 10: 1989756719

For Riley,
our beloved teacher

Riley, my friend, let's walk and talk, see and feel, stretch and sense all of the wonderful wonders in our neighborhood.

Step Step Step

Our feet take steps on the sidewalk.
Cleo the cat comes to say hi.

Riley and I stretch like a cat ... can you?

Bubba's tail wags back and forth.
He's so happy to see us!

Riley and I stretch like a dog ... can you?

Wind Wind Wind

We feel the wind on our skin.
We see a butterfly
floating on the breeze.

Riley and I stretch like a butterfly ... can you?

Oh, how we love to stop and sniff the flowers that greet us!

Riley and I stretch like a flower.
Can you stretch like a flower too?

Up
Up
Up

The tree stretches its branches
up towards the sky.

Riley and I stretch our arms like branches and our legs like roots. Can you stretch like a tree too?

Zoom

Zoom

Zoom

We hear an airplane flying high in the sky.

Riley and I stretch like an airplane ... can you?

Flap
Flap
Flap

A pigeon flies down to greet us.

Riley and I stretch like a pigeon ... can you?

Giggle

Giggle

Giggle

Happy Baby

Our friend, baby Sage, is so happy.

Riley and I stretch like a happy baby ... can you?

Breathe

Breathe

Breathe

Riley and I place our hands on our
chests and stomachs. We feel our breath
move in and out, up and down.

Can you feel your breath
move in and out, up and down?

We are so thankful for
cats, dogs, butterflies,
flowers, trees, airplanes,
birds, babies,
and especially our friendship.

Love
Love
Love

Riley, my friend, thank you for this walk.
I love you.

Cary and Stacey are sisters, best friends, and grateful students of the canine teachers in their lives. By combining their skills in education, health, and mindfulness, they are able to offer a holistic approach to providing transformative teachings and resources for kids. It is their heartfelt intention to have a positive impact on all beings in mind, body and spirit.

To learn more please visit CarySaltsgaver.com

With every donation, a voice will be given to
the creativity that lies within the hearts of
our children living with diverse challenges.

By making this difference, children that may
not have been given the opportunity to have their
Heart Heard will have the freedom to create
beautiful works of art and musical creations.

Donate by visiting
HeartstobeHeard.com

We thank you.

In praise of **Riley's Yoga Walk**

"*Riley's Yoga Walk* is an amazing blend of yoga, art, and mindfulness. Cary is a passionate teacher of all ages, from preschool to adults. The magic of learning she creates for little ones and teachers has inspired thousands. I have been so fortunate to learn from Cary and strongly recommend reading *Riley's Yoga Walk* and attending her workshops."

> – **Dr. Brett Geithman**, Superintendent, Larkspur-Corte Madera School District

"As an educational leader, I am always looking to share resources with teachers and principals that align with our school district's vision, mission, and goals. *Riley's Yoga Walk* beautifully supports our commitment to promote social and emotional wellness and nurture our culture of care. I can't wait to share *Riley's Yoga Walk* with our community and... my own family :-)."

> – **Katherine Whittaker Stopp**, Assistant Superintendent of Educational Services
> Manhattan Beach Unified School District

"Too often we move through life carrying the stresses of the world on our shoulders and in our hearts. *Riley's Yoga Walk* teaches us to slow down and appreciate those things we encounter on a simple walk around the neighborhood. We come away feeling lighter, relaxed and happier because of it."

> – **Chris Rodenhizer**, Former Principal and Professional Developer for Elementary Schools

"If you would like to walk with the real deal, Cary Saltsgaver of *Riley's Yoga Walk* is just that. She embodies the spirit of life as she breathes inspiration to youngsters as they glide alongside Riley on their yoga journey."

> – **Tara Thomas**, Co-founder, Momentum in Teaching

"For parents who see the value of introducing mindfulness and mindfulness practices to their children, this book will prove a wonderful resource. Combining kids, dogs, yoga and a whole lotta love, this book is a great way to introduce kids to the positive influences of yoga and other mindfulness practices. I highly recommend."

> – **Charley Allen**, Psychotherapist and Mindfulness Teacher

"In their debut children's book, sisters, Cary Saltsgaver and Stacey Harris, have teamed up to combine their expertise in mindfulness, yoga, and art to create a beautiful book that will resonate with adults and children of all ages. I highly recommend adding this book to your library. It's sure to become a classic. Undoubtedly, you will want to share this book with loved ones as well. I can't wait to see what Riley is up to next!"

> – **Rebecca West**, PhD, APRN, FNP-BC, Board certified Family Nurse Practitioner
> Mindfulness Meditation Teacher, Hatha Yoga instructor, Health and Wellness Coach

Riley and I would love to hear from you!

Draw or write about your favorite part of the book.
Please visit CarySaltsgaver.com to share it with us!

Lightning Source UK Ltd.
Milton Keynes UK
UKHW050707271120
374182UK00002B/23